M000113073

The Christian and the Bible

Growing Through the Study of God's Word

STEP 5

Bill Bright

NewLife
PUBLICATIONS
A MINISTRY OF CAMPUS CRUSADE FOR CHRIST

Ten Basic Steps Toward Christian Maturity
Step 5: The Christian and the Bible

Published by
New*Life* Publications
375 Highway 74 South, Suite A
Peachtree City, GA 30269

© 1994, Bill Bright. All rights reserved. No part of this publication may be reproduced, stored in a retrieval system, or transmitted in any form or by any means, except in the case of brief quotations printed in articles or reviews, without prior permission in writing from the publisher.

Printed in the United States of America.

ISBN: 1–56399–034–2

Thomas Nelson Inc., Nashville, Tennessee, is the exclusive distributor of this book to the trade markets in the United States and the District of Columbia.

Distributed in Canada by Campus Crusade for Christ of Canada, Surrey, B.C.

Unless otherwise indicated, all Scripture references are from the *New International Version*, © 1973, 1978, 1984 by the International Bible Society. Published by Zondervan Bible Publishers, Grand Rapids, Michigan.

Scripture quotations designated NKJ are from the *New King James* version, © 1979, 1980, 1982 by Thomas Nelson Inc., Publishers, Nashville, Tennessee.

Scripture quotations designated Phillips are from *Letters to Young Churches, A Translation of the New Testament Epistles*, by J. B. Phillips, © 1947, 1957 by the MacMillan Company, New York, New York.

Any royalties from this book or the many other books by Bill Bright are dedicated to the glory of God and designated to the various ministries of Campus Crusade for Christ/*NewLife2000*.

For more information, write:

L.I.F.E.—P. O. Box 40, Flemmington Markets, 2129, Australia
Campus Crusade for Christ of Canada—Box 300, Vancouver, B.C., V6C 2X3, Canada
Campus Crusade for Christ—Fairgate House, King's Road, Tyseley, Birmingham, B11 2AA, England
Lay Institute for Evangelism—P. O. Box 8786, Auckland 3, New Zealand
Campus Crusade for Christ—Alexandra, P. O. Box 0205, Singapore 9115, Singapore
Great Commission Movement of Nigeria—P. O. Box 500, Jos, Plateau State Nigeria, West Africa
Campus Crusade for Christ International—100 Sunport Lane, Orlando, FL 32809, USA

Contents

Acknowledgments

The *Ten Basic Steps Toward Christian Maturity* series was a product of necessity. As the ministry of Campus Crusade for Christ expanded rapidly to scores of campuses across America, thousands of students committed their lives to Christ—several hundred on a single campus. Individual follow-up of all new converts soon became impossible. Who was to help them grow in their new-found faith?

A Bible study series designed for new Christians was desperately needed—a study that would stimulate individuals and groups to explore the depths and the riches of God's Word. Although several excellent studies were available, we felt the particular need of new material for these college students.

In 1955, I asked several of my fellow staff associates to assist me in the preparation of Bible studies that would stimulate both evangelism and Christian growth in a new believer. The contribution by campus staff members was especially significant because of their constant contact with students in introducing them to Christ and meeting regularly with them to disciple them. Thus, the *Ten Basic Steps Toward Christian Maturity* was the fruit of our combined labor.

Since that modest beginning, many other members of the staff have contributed generously. On occasion, for example, I found myself involved in research and writing sessions with several of our staff, all seminary graduates, some with advanced degrees and one with his doctorate in theology. More important, all were actively engaged in "winning, building, and sending men" for Christ.

For this latest edition, I want to thank Don Tanner for his professional assistance in revising, expanding, and editing the contents. I also want to thank Joette Whims and Jean Bryant for their extensive help and for joining Don and me in the editorial process.

A Personal Word

A dear friend of mine, Dr. Henrietta Mears, was one of the greatest influences on my life. She was instrumental in introducing me and my wife, Vonette, to Jesus Christ. I admired her dearly and I miss her deeply since she went to be with the Lord.

Dr. Mears had a deep awe and respect for God's holy Word. Living her life by the Word, she wrote a book entitled *What the Bible Is All About*, which has sold more than three million copies. She described the Bible this way:

> The Bible is one book, one history, one story, His story. Behind 10,000 events stands God, the builder of history, the maker of the ages. Eternity bounds the one side, eternity bounds the other side, and time is in between: Genesis—origins, Revelation—endings, and all the way between, God is working things out. You can go down into the minutest detail everywhere and see that there is one great purpose moving through the ages: the eternal design of the Almighty God to redeem a wrecked and ruined world.[1]

To find out more about God, His plan for us, and our wonderful Savior, we need to read and meditate on the Bible every day and

---

[1] Henrietta C. Mears, *What the Bible Is All About* (Ventura, CA: Regal Books, 1983), p.20.

apply its truths to our lifestyle. We need to hold it as the anchor of our attitudes and actions. But we cannot pull from one part of God's Word and disregard other sections. Dr. Mears wrote:

> The Bible is one book, and you cannot take it in texts and expect to comprehend the magnificence of divine revelation. You must see it in its completeness. God has taken pains to give us a progressive revelation and we should take pains to read it from beginning to end. Don't suppose reading little scraps can ever be compensation for doing deep and consecutive work on the Bible itself. We must get back to the Book and then we will not tolerate such work.

The kind of respect we have for God's Word makes the difference. A famous actor was at a party one evening when a clergyman asked him to recite the 23rd Psalm. The actor, an eloquent star of stage and screen, agreed on one condition: that the clergyman, a man in his eighties who had served God faithfully and humbly for more than half a century, would also recite the Psalm.

The minister agreed, and the actor began his recitation. Oh, the words came like beautiful music, and everyone was enthralled as he gave a magnificent presentation. When he finished, the audience applauded heartily.

Then the minister stood. He was not eloquent; he was not a particularly gifted speaker. But as he began to recite the 23rd Psalm, a hush fell over the audience, and tears began to moisten their cheeks. When he finished, there was no applause. Only silence.

The actor stood to his feet and concluded, "I have reached your ears, but this man of God has reached your heart."

I think we all admire a life like that—so in love with God that the Bible has richly penetrated his heart. But you may be saying, "I can't even begin to picture myself having such a deep and personal relationship with God. I fall far short of that."

Do you desire to be a man or woman of God? You can be if you make reading and studying God's Word a priority in your life. The more time you spend in His Word, and the more consistently you obey God's commands, the faster you will grow in your Christian life.

I have been a Christian for nearly fifty years, and I still have much to learn. I am not perfect yet! And I do not expect to be in this life. But the more I take the time to study God's Word and obey His instructions, the more I become like Christ, His Son.

By spending just a few minutes a day in personal Bible reading, your life will change. After reading God's Word consistently for several months, you will be amazed by the things God has done in your life.

Many people who have been Christians for years find themselves setting the Bible aside, and before they know it, God seems distant. This may be you. Or perhaps you are a new Christian and you have never made the effort to consistently read God's Word.

Let me challenge you to do one thing today that could change your life. Take out your Bible. Then make this commitment to God: spend at least five minutes a day reading His Word. Get to know the God of the Bible, the creator of the universe—our loving personal Lord.

You can read the entire New Testament in approximately twenty-five hours. You may want to set a goal of reading it during the next thirty days. As an excited new Christian, a dear friend read the New Testament from Matthew to Revelation during a forty-eight hour period. Ask the Lord to guide you in the amount of time you set aside each day to read His Word.

I suggest that you begin reading in the Gospel of John. You may have read it several times before, but as you seek God with a hungry heart, willing to learn, it will be new and challenging.

I have prepared these lessons on God's Word because I want to help you experience a closer walk with our Lord and become a fruitful witness for Him. What a privilege you and I have to communicate with the Almighty Creator-God, our loving heavenly Father. He is waiting right now to speak to you.

God bless you as you learn the principles outlined in the Step. As you sit at His feet and obey what He will say through His living inspired Word, your life will be changed forever.

Bill Bright

What This Study Will Do for You

The Bible is by far the best-selling book of all time. No other book comes close in the number of copies printed and distributed. Many Bibles are passed down from one generation to the next.

God's holy, inspired Word has been translated into thousands of different languages and dialects. And there are certainly more books written about the Bible than any other work in the history of man.

But let's be very honest. The handsome leather-bound books that decorate the coffee tables, bookshelves, and bedstands of American homes rarely leave those positions—with the exception of a token visit to church on Sunday morning.

Many well-intentioned believers neglect God's Word because they do not know how to study it and apply its truths consistently to their lives. In this Step, I want to share with you key principles for getting the most from God's Word and making your Bible study a fulfilling and exciting spiritual adventure.

You will benefit from this study in three ways:

First, *you will discover why the Bible is God's unique, inspired Word to man.* You will be introduced to the central person of the Bible. You will examine the trustworthiness

❖

You will learn to depend on the power of God's Word for your daily Christian living.

of the Scripture and gain confidence in its authority concerning the issues of your life.

Second, *the Bible will become a living book to you.* As you view the power of God's Word, you will learn to depend on it for your daily Christian living. The Bible is filled with precious promises that you can claim as a believer. These life-changing truths will transform you into a vibrant, fruitful Christian as you grow in supernatural wisdom and spiritual insight.

Third, *you will learn to establish good habits of regular, systematic study of the Bible.* These lessons will help you develop a proper attitude for Bible study. And you will examine several methods for studying God's Word that will revolutionize your understanding of the Bible.

Foundation for Faith

Step 5: The Christian and the Bible is part of the *Ten Basic Steps Toward Christian Maturity,* a time-tested study series designed to provide you with a sure foundation for your faith. Hundreds of thousands have benefited from this Bible study series during the almost forty years since it was first published in its original form.

When you complete Step 5, I encourage you to continue your study with the rest of the Steps.

If you are a new Christian, the *Ten Basic Steps* will acquaint you with the major doctrines of the Christian faith. By applying the principles you will learn, you will grow spiritually and find solutions to problems you are likely to face as a new believer.

If you are a mature Christian, you will discover the tools you need to help others receive Christ and grow in their faith. Your own commitment to our Lord will be affirmed, and you will discover how to develop an effective devotional and study plan.

The series includes an individual booklet for the introductory study and one for each of the ten Steps. These study guides correlate with the expanded and updated *Handbook for Christian Maturity* and *Ten Basic Steps Leader's Guide.*

Each Step reveals a different facet of the Christian life and truth, and each contains lessons for study that can be used during your personal quiet time or in a group setting.

I encourage you to pursue the study of Step 5 with an open, eager mind. As you read, continually pray that the Holy Spirit will give you a greater sense of your need for the Word of God to help you live victoriously and fruitfully for our Lord.

How to Use This Study

On page 14 of this Step, you will find the preparatory article, "Living By the Book." The article will give you a clear perspective on how you can study God's Word effectively and release its power in your daily life and Christian service. Read it carefully before you begin Lesson 1. Review it prayerfully during your study.

This Step contains seven lessons plus a "Recap" or review. Each lesson is divided into two sections: the Bible Study and the Life Application. Begin by noting the Objective for the lesson you are studying. The Objective states the main goal for your study. Keep it in mind as you continue through the lesson.

Appropriate memory verse references have been provided to help you in your walk with Christ. Learn each verse by writing it on a small card to carry with you. You can buy cards for these verses at any bookstore or print shop, or you can make your own by using filing cards. Review daily the verses you have memorized.

Our Lord has commanded that we learn His Word. Proverbs 7:1–3 reminds us:

> My son, keep my words and store up my commands within you. Keep my commands and you will live; guard my teachings

Your most important objective is to meet with God in a loving, personal way.

as the apple of your eye. Bind them on your fingers; write
them on the tablet of your heart.

As you meditate on the verses you have memorized and claim
God's promises, you will experience the joy, victory, and power
that God's Word gives to your Christian walk. When you have
finished all the studies in the entire series, you will be able to
develop your own Bible study, continuing to use a systematic method for memorizing God's Word.

How to Study the Lessons

Casual Bible reading uncovers valuable spiritual facts that lie near
the surface. But understanding the deeper truths requires study.
Often the difference between reading and studying is a pen and
notepad.

Every lesson in this study covers an important topic and gives
you an opportunity to record your answers to the questions. Plan to
spend a minimum of thirty minutes each day—preferably in the
morning—in Bible study, meditation, and prayer.

Remember, the most important objective and benefit of a quiet
time or Bible study is not to acquire knowledge or accumulate
biblical information but to meet with God in a loving, personal way.

Here are some suggestions to help you in your study time:

◆ Plan a specific time and place to work on these studies. Make
  an appointment with God; then keep it.

◆ Use a pen or pencil, your Bible, and this booklet.

◆ Begin with prayer for God's presence, blessing, and wisdom.

◆ Meditate on the Objective to determine how it fits into your
  circumstances.

◆ Memorize the suggested verses.

◆ Proceed to the Bible study, trusting God to use it to teach you.
  Prayerfully anticipate His presence with you. Work carefully,
  reading the Scripture passages and thinking through the
  questions. Answer each as completely as possible.

◆ When you come to the Life Application, answer the questions
  honestly and begin to apply them to your own life.

♦ Prayerfully read through the lesson again and reevaluate your Life Application answers. Do they need changing? Or adjusting?

♦ Review the memory verses.

♦ Consider the Objective again and determine if it has been accomplished. If not, what do you need to do?

♦ Close with a prayer of thanksgiving, and ask God to help you grow spiritually in the areas He has specifically revealed to you.

♦ When you complete the first seven lessons of this Step, spend extra time on the Recap to make sure you understand every lesson thoroughly.

♦ If you need more study of this Step, ask God for wisdom again and go through whatever lesson(s) you need to review, repeating the process until you do understand and are able to apply the truths to your own life.

These studies are not intended as a complete development of Christian beliefs. However, a careful study of the material will give you, with God's help, a sufficient understanding of how you can know and apply God's plan for your life. By applying the principles you learn in this study, you will gain greater confidence in the authority and power of God's holy Word.

Do not rush through the lessons. Take plenty of time to think through the questions. Meditate on them. Absorb the truths presented, and make the application a part of your life. Give God a chance to speak to you, and let the Holy Spirit teach you. As you spend time with our Lord in prayer and study, and as you trust and obey Him, you will experience the amazing joy of His presence (John 14:21).

Living By the Book

Have you ever had a time when you thought you knew where you were going but got lost instead? Maybe you were in an unfamiliar area and took a wrong turn. It was late and the sun had gone down. Everything looked different in the dark. As you drove up and down the streets looking for the address, you searched the glove compartment for a map—but you had left it at home. How you wish you had not assumed you knew where you were going!

We take so many things in life for granted. We do not realize, for example, the blessings of health until we experience the pain of illness. Our eyes are often closed to the dearness of those we love until they are gone. And most of us fail to realize the awesome privilege it is to have a Bible—a book that does not merely *contain* the Word of God, but in fact *is* the holy, inspired Word of God.

That we even have a Bible is a marvelous privilege most of us take for granted. Many governments have openly discouraged or forbidden their citizens to read the powerful truths of God's Word. Officials have shut down Bible printing presses and arrested Christians who smuggle Bibles across their borders. Thank God this is changing in many

"The Bible is an armory of heavenly weapons,... a mine of exhaustless wealth."

parts of the world, where for the first time in many decades, God's Word is being welcomed openly and warmly.

Another blessing is that we have a Bible in our own language. Numerous translations of the Bible are available to us in English. But in hundreds of regions around the world, God's Word has not yet been translated into the native language or dialect. With no knowledge of His Word, millions of people live in spiritual darkness and ignorance.

A third blessing is that we are financially able to own our own copy of the Bible. Many of us have several copies. Multitudes around the world cannot afford such a luxury, however. Our staff leaders in Central Asia, for example, often work with earnest, devoted Christians whose sole exposure to Christ is the "JESUS" Film, a two-hour film depicting the life of Christ based on the Gospel of Luke. Aside from that marvelous evangelistic tool, they have no other spiritual material. In some areas, an entire village may have to share a single copy of the Scripture, and most villages have none at all.

What God reveals through His Word is yet another blessing. Since the Bible is God's revelation of Himself to man, we know that Christ is God, that He came to earth to die for our sins, and that He arose from the dead and now lives in every believer. We have knowledge of the person and ministry of the Holy Spirit, who empowers us to live holy lives and be fruitful witnesses for the Lord Jesus. Because of God's Word, we know how to pray, to repent of our sins, and to experience the love and forgiveness of God through faith in our Lord.

I cannot overemphasize the value of God's Word to our daily life. The Scottish pastor and writer Thomas Cuthrie expressed it well:

> The Bible is an armory of heavenly weapons, a laboratory of infallible medicines, a mine of exhaustless wealth. It is a guidebook for every road, a chart for every sea, a medicine for every malady, and a balm for every wound. Rob us of our Bible, and our sky has lost its sun.

The great evangelist D. L. Moody said:

> I prayed for faith, and thought that some day faith would come down and strike me like lightning. But faith

did not seem to come. One day I read in the tenth chapter of Romans, "Now faith comes by hearing, and hearing by the Word of God." I had closed my Bible and prayed for faith. I now opened my Bible and began to study, and faith has been growing every since.

And George Mueller, a great man of faith, expressed his love for God's Word by saying:

The vigor of our spiritual life will be in exact proportion to the place held by the Bible in our life and thoughts …I have read the Bible through 100 times, and always with increasing delight. Each time it seems like a new book to me. Great has been the blessing from consecutive, diligent, daily study. I look upon it as a lost day when I have not had a good time over the Word of God.

No doubt you are familiar with the book *Mutiny on the Bounty.* Captain Bligh miraculously lived after the mutiny and returned to England to report the crime. Many of the guilty sailors were found and hanged. Several, however, could not be found.

Twenty years passed and the whole incident was forgotten until a ship discovered an uncharted island. When the crew landed, they could hardly believe what they had found: an utter utopia. No disease, no crime, no drunkenness, just grace and harmony.

When the crew learned the reason for the behavior of the islanders, they were amazed. Eight of the Bounty's sailors had fled to this island after the mutiny. They had ravaged the people and all but one of the sailors, Alexander Smith, had died.

In desperation he had rummaged through all of the other men's belongings, looking for more whiskey, when he found a Bible. He read it, believed it, and became a Christian. He introduced the entire population of the island to Christ and they, with him, believed and obeyed the Word of God.

God's Word not only influences men's actions—it transforms men's lives. We need to study the Word effectively and carefully and interpret it correctly so that we not only possess its truths, but its truths possess us.

Have you ever been uncertain about something you read in the Bible? Have you been at a loss for words when a friend has questioned you over the correct interpretation of a Bible passage?

Students of the Bible sometimes find themselves confused over how to interpret Scripture. But let me assure you that there are sound ways for determining the meaning of God's Word.

As a child of God, you have the Holy Spirit to guide you into all truth as you search the Scriptures. Before you begin each Bible study period, ask the Holy Spirit to guide you. Look at the verse you are reading in its historical setting. Study the culture of the time. Ask yourself these questions: To whom was it written? Does the passage deal only with a specific period in history or does it apply to me as well?

Interpret a book, chapter, or verse in the Bible in light of its original meaning. Determine the meaning of the words or passages that are unclear to you with the use of Bible study tools such as a lexicon, concordance, Bible dictionary, or commentary. You can obtain these tools from your local Christian bookstore or check them out of your church library.

Examine the text in light of other Scripture portions that deal with the same subject. The Bible does not contradict itself. If you want to learn what it says about the doctrine of hell, for example, read several passages that refer to hell. It is a mistake to create a theology based on only one or two verses of Scripture.

As you study, ask yourself the following questions:

- Who or what is the main subject of the passage?
- To whom or what is it referring?
- What is the key verse?
- What does the passage teach about Jesus Christ?
- Does it bring to light personal sin that you need to confess and forsake?
- Does the Scripture portion contain a command for you to obey?
- Does it hold a promise for you to claim?

I urge you to begin adopting these principles of interpretation when studying God's Word. As a person who is able to correctly interpret the Word of God to believers and non-believers alike, you will become a better witness for our Lord.

Each time I begin my study, I ask the Holy Spirit, who inspired holy men of old to record these sacred truths, to make them real in my experience. I ask the Holy Spirit to help me understand what each passage means. Then I apply these truths to my own life. I study the Word with an open mind and a thirst for truth. I approach my study with a contrite heart. Trusting the Holy Spirit to make the cleansing power of His Word come alive within me, I am eager to obey all that He commands.

The Psalmist wrote, "I have hidden your word in my heart that I might not sin against you" (Psalm 119:11). Let me encourage you to begin hiding the Word of God in your heart. Early each morning or before you go to bed at night, spend time alone with God and His precious Word. Mark the verses in your Bible that are especially meaningful to you, and commit them to memory. Meditate on these verses until they become part of you. Get involved in a small Bible study group where you can receive systematic teaching.

I can assure you that as you take time to study His Word and enjoy His wonderful love and fellowship, your life will be trans-formed by the power of the Holy Spirit.

As you study the lessons in this Step, I urge you to thank God for providing you with a Bible. Thank Him for the freedom you enjoy in studying and reading His holy Word daily. And share the wonder-ful life-changing truths you learn with your friends, loved ones, and fellow students or workers.

The Book of Books

The Bible is God's holy, inspired Word. It is the most powerful and most quoted book in the world. Some of the greatest men in modern history have had a deep respect for the Bible:

> *Abraham Lincoln:* "I believe the Bible is the best gift God has ever given to man. All the good from the Savior of the world is communicated to us through this Book."

> *Immanuel Kant:* "The existence of the Bible, as a book for people, is the greatest benefit which the human race has ever experienced. Every attempt to belittle it is a crime against humanity."

> *Robert E. Lee:* "In all my perplexities and distresses, the Bible has never failed to give me light and strength."

> *Daniel Webster:* "If there is anything in my thought or style to commend, the credit is due to my parents for instilling in me early love for the Scriptures."

Hundreds of millions of people have read its sacred pages, making it the best-selling book of all time.

The composition of the Bible is indeed amazing. A library of sixty-six books, it was

Objective: To recognize the unparalleled composition of the Bible and become familiar with its structure

Read: Acts 15 and 16

Memorize: 2 Timothy 3:16,17

written by forty different human authors under the divine inspiration of the Holy Spirit. These writers wrote independently, knowing almost nothing of the others' part. None had anything in common, and their literary qualifications were diverse. Moses, for example, was a man of learning, trained in the best universities of Egypt. Peter, on the other hand, was a fisherman without claim to formal education. Yet each wrote the wisdom of God with powerful force.

It took the Old and New Testament writers fifteen centuries to complete the Bible, which was written in three languages (Hebrew, Aramaic, and Greek) on three continents. Indeed, this collection of books is really one, not sixty-six, for it is coherent in content and progressive in truth.

The Bible is composed of 1189 chapters (929 in the Old Testament and 260 in the New Testament) and utilizes 773,746 words to convey its life-changing message. This literary masterpiece contains history, laws, poetry, prophecy, biography, dramatic stories, letters, and revelations. In the words of Sir Isaac Newton:

> There are more sure marks of authenticity in the Bible than in any profane history.

Christian Church leaders of the fifth century A.D. decided upon the list of books to be included in the Bible. This collection of accepted writings came to be known by scholars as the "canon," and were considered inspired and authoritative.

In this lesson you will study the various names of the Bible, survey the construction of the Old and New Testaments, and gain insights that will make your own Bible study more meaningful.

Bible Study

Various Names of the Bible

List the various names the Bible is called according to the following references:

1 Corinthians 15:3,4

Ephesians 6:17

Construction of the Bible

1. To become familiar with your own Bible, leaf through it and look at these divisions and books as you progress through the lesson. If possible, use a Bible with headlines to help you answer the questions.

The Bible is composed of two main sections: the Old Testament, containing 39 books, and the New Testament, containing 27 books.

2. Read Genesis 1 and Revelation 22. From these two chapters, summarize the scope of the contents of the Bible.

Divisions of the Old Testament

The Old Testament can be divided into five parts:

1. *Pentateuch.* The first five historical books, written by Moses, also are called the books of the Law. List these books:

Identify at least four major events recorded in these books.

2. *Historical Books.* The next twelve books tell of the establishment of the kingdom of Israel, of Israel's repeated turning from God to sin, and finally of the Assyrian and Babylonian exile—God's punishment. List these twelve books as follows and identify a main character in each section:

First three (pre-kingdom era):

Next six (duration of the kingdom):

Last three (exile and post-exile period):

3. *Poetry.* Of the next five books, Psalms—the Hebrew hymn book—is probably the best known. List the five books of poetry.

Describe how God has used one of these books to comfort and strengthen you in a difficult situation.

4. *Major Prophets.* Written shortly before Israel was taken into captivity and during the exile, these books prophesy the coming Messiah and other world events. They also contain warnings of impending disaster if Israel did not turn from her wicked ways. List the five books of the Major Prophets.

Identify at least one major prophecy in each.

5. *Minor Prophets.* These last twelve books of the Old Testament are called minor only because they are shorter, not because they are less important. They mainly concern Israel and the coming Messiah. List all twelve:

Read one of the books and summarize its main points.

Divisions of the New Testament

The New Testament can also be divided into five parts.

1. *Gospels.* The first four books of the New Testament tell of Christ's life and ministry. List them here:

What was Jesus' last command to His disciples
(Matthew 28:19,20)?

How does this apply today?

2. *Acts.* This history of the early church, which also describes
the ministries of Peter and Paul, consists of only one book.
For practice, write it here:

What is its significance for us today?

3. *Pauline Epistles and Hebrews.* Thirteen of the epistles
(letters) were written by Paul, and were named for the
church or individual to whom they were sent. Although the
author of Hebrews is not identified, many believe Paul also
wrote that fourteenth epistle. List all fourteen.

Write down your favorite verse in each book and describe why it is meaningful to you.

4. *General Epistles.* There are seven general epistles, and they are named not for the recipients but for the authors. List them here:

Identify one major truth in each book, and tell how you will apply each truth to your life.

5. *Revelation.* The last book of the New Testament is one of prophecy. It describes the end times and the triumph of Christ in His second coming. Write the name of it here:

Describe the central message of the book (Revelation 22:12–17).

What are its promises to those who overcome (chapters 2,3)?

What warning does the writer of this book give (22:18,19)?

LIFE APPLICATION

❶ What new insight about the composition of the Bible have you gained from this study?

How will this help you in your daily life?

❷ To know the Bible well and to be able to find Scripture references quickly, you should memorize the names of the books in the order in which they appear. Master one group, and then go on to the next.

Focus on one division each week until you have memorized all the books of the Bible. Review these frequently until they are fixed in your mind.

Today, commit to memory the books of the first division, the Pentateuch, and write them again here:

1)

2)

3)

4)

5)

❖   ❖   ❖

The Central Person of the Bible

Jesus is the most remarkable and fascinating person in history. He has inspired more hope, taught more compassion, and shown more love than any other man who has ever lived.

Jesus is the central figure of the Bible. His birth as the Jewish Messiah and Savior of the world was prophesied by Old Testament authors. Their writings contain more than three hundred separate references to the coming of Jesus, with many unique details. Christ fulfilled 100 percent of all the Old Testament predictions of the birth, life, death, and resurrection of the Messiah.

Objective: To recognize the entire Bible as God's revelation of Jesus Christ to us

Read: Acts 17 and 18

Memorize: 1 Corinthians 15:3,4

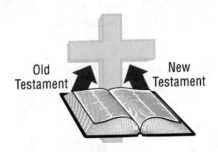

Old Testament   New Testament

The New Testament makes an even more revolutionary claim: that Jesus Christ is the center of all biblical prophecy. The Scripture proclaims:

29

> Long ago God spoke in many different ways to our
> fathers through the prophets [in visions, dreams, and
> even face to face], telling them little by little about his
> plans. But now in these days he has spoken to us through
> his Son to whom he has given everything, and through
> whom he made the world and everything there is
> (Hebrews 1:1,2).

And the Book of Ephesians declares:

> God has told us his secret reason for sending Christ,
> a plan he decided on in mercy long ago; and this was his
> purpose: that when the time is ripe he will gather us all
> together from wherever we are—in heaven or on earth—
> to be with him in Christ, forever (Ephesians 1:9,10).

The precise fulfillment of the immense body of biblical prophecy
is found in one unique and revolutionary Man—Jesus of Nazareth.
Claiming that He was the predicted One of old, Jesus stepped into
time. And the pieces of the prophetic puzzle slipped into place. We
can clearly see that He was the center of God's revelation to man.

Bible Study

What Christ Said About Himself and the Old Testament

1. What did Christ say of the Scriptures in John 5:39?

2. Read Luke 24:25–27, 44–48.

What was Christ's claim concerning the Old Testament
teaching about Himself?

What parts of the Old Testament did Christ say referred to
Him (verse 44)?

What do you think Christ wants you to understand about the Old Testament from verse 26?

From verses 46, 47?

What the Apostles Said About Christ and the Old Testament

1. What does Peter conclude in Acts 3:18?

2. Keeping in mind that the New Testament had not yet been written, how did the apostle Paul use the Old Testament to show that it contained the "good news" of Christ (Acts 17:1–3)?

3. What three things occurred in Christ's life that Paul said were taught in the Old Testament (1 Corinthians 15:3,4)?

1)

2)

3)

4. What does Paul conclude in Romans 15:8,9 about the ministry of Christ?

Old Testament Prophecies Concerning Christ Fulfilled in the New Testament

All of the more than 300 Old Testament prophecies about the first coming of the Messiah were fulfilled in the life of Christ. Here are a few of them.

1. Compare these Scripture references and record the prophecies fulfilled.

COMPARE	WITH	FULFILLMENT
1 Samuel 16:19 Isaiah 11:1	Luke 1:31–33	
Genesis 3:15	Galatians 4:4 Hebrews 2:14	
Numbers 24:17	Matthew 2:2,9	
Isaiah 9:6	Matthew 1:23	
Isaiah 40:3	Matthew 3:1–3	
Zechariah 9:9	Matthew 21:1–11	
Psalm 69:21	Matthew 27:34	
Psalm 34:20	John 19:33,36	
Job 19:25–27	Galatians 3:13 1 John 3:2	

2. What is your impression after seeing these Old Testament prophecies and their New Testament fulfillment?

Christ, the Central Person of the New Testament

1. The four Gospels are the history books of Christ's ministry. (Read Matthew 1:1; Mark 1:1; Luke 1:1–4; John 20:30,31.)

   In what ways did the disciples know Jesus (1 John 1:3)?

   Do the four Gospels purport to record all that Jesus did (John 20:30)?

   Why were the historical facts and teachings of Jesus Christ written (John 20:31)?

2. The Book of Acts is a historical account of the acts of the Holy Spirit through the apostles.

   Who wrote it (Luke 1:1–4 and Acts 1:1)?

   How do you think the passage in Luke applies to the Book of Acts?

3. The Epistles are letters written to show the church the practical outworking of the life of Christ in the lives of those who wrote them. By example, they teach us regarding our membership in the body of Christ, and about our privileges, responsibilities, and destiny.

   Read Colossians 2:6–8.

   What are Christians to do?

How are we to do it?

Of what are we to beware?

What would you say our greatest responsibility is?

4. The Book of Revelation is the only New Testament book of prophecy. Read Revelation 1:1–3.
This book is the revelation of whom?

What is its purpose?

Who gave such knowledge?

How was this knowledge given, and to whom?

How will studying the Book of Revelation affect your life and under what conditions?

LIFE APPLICATION

1 How will recognizing Jesus as the central figure of the entire Bible affect your Old Testament reading?

2 What do you see as your individual responsibility in fulfilling the commands of this person? See John 15:16 and Matthew 28:19,20.

3 Memorize the twelve Historical Books and write them again here:

Pre-kingdom era (3)

Kingdom era (6)

Exile and post-exile era (3)

Review the names of all the books learned earlier.

Authority of the Old Testament

Researchers in Israel recently subjected the first five books of the Old Testament to exhaustive computer analysis. They came to a different conclusion than expected.

Skeptics had long assumed that the Torah, or Books of Moses, was the work of multiple authors. But Scripture scholar Moshe Katz and computer expert Menachem Wiener of the Israel Institute of Technology refuted this belief. They discovered an intricate pattern of significant words concealed in the canon, spelled by letters separated at fixed intervals.

According to Katz, the statistical possibility of such patterns happening by chance would be one in three million. The material, he said, suggests a single, inspired author—in fact, it could not have been put together by human capabilities at all. "So we need a non-rational explanation," he said. "And ours is that the Torah was written by God through the hand of Moses."

The Old Testament was considered by its writers to be the inspired and authoritative Word of God. Our Lord Himself, the New Testament writers, and the early church also affirmed its authenticity.

❖

Objective: To gain confidence in the trustworthiness of the Bible by examining the authority of the Old Testament

Read: Acts 19 and 20

Memorize: 2 Peter 1:20,21

Of Moses it is said, "Moses then wrote down everything the Lord had said" (Exodus 24:4). David said, "The Spirit of the Lord spoke through me; his word was on my tongue" (2 Samuel 23:2). The prophet Jeremiah said, "The word of the Lord came to me, saying…" (Jeremiah 1:4). Ezekiel, Daniel, and Amos made it perfectly clear that their messages were absolutely and wholly from God.

Jesus frequently referred to Old Testament Scriptures during His earthly ministry. In confronting the unbelief of the Jews, Jesus affirmed that the "Scripture cannot be broken" (John 10:35). During His Sermon on the Mount, Jesus said, "I tell you the

"Thus saith the Lord"
2,000 times in Old Testament

truth, until heaven and earth disappear, not the smallest letter, not the least stroke of a pen, will by any means disappear from the Law until everything is accomplished" (Matthew 5:18).

While teaching in the temple courts, Jesus cited Psalm 110:1 and declared that David spoke by the Holy Spirit (Mark 12:35,36). After His resurrection, Jesus said to His disciples, "This is what I told you while I was still with you: Everything must be fulfilled that is written about me in the Law of Moses, the Prophets and the Psalms." Then Luke notes, "He opened their minds so they could understand the Scriptures" (Luke 24:44,45). The Jews used the expression, "The Law, the Prophets, and the Psalms" to represent the entire Old Testament.

Concerning the birth of Christ, Matthew records, "All this took place to fulfill what the Lord had said through the prophet" (Matthew 1:22). In quoting the song of Zechariah (the father of John Baptist) concerning the birth of Jesus, Luke included the affirmation, "as he said through his holy prophets of long ago" (Luke 1:70). And the writer of Acts records Peter's speech concerning the fate of Judas who betrayed Jesus, "Brothers, the Scripture had to be fulfilled which the Holy Spirit spoke long ago through the mouth of David" (Acts 1:16).

Many other passages testify to the authority of the Old Testament, often with the words, "that the Scripture might be fulfilled" (John 19:24,36) or "for this is what the prophet has written" (Matthew 2:5). Peter affirmed, "No prophecy of Scripture came about by the prophet's own interpretation. For prophecy never had its origin in the will of man, but men spoke from God as they were carried along by the Holy Spirit" (2 Peter 1:20,21).

As the early church grew, differences in doctrines surfaced. But no matter how much the church fathers differed in their teachings, they were unanimous in one thing: that in the entire Old Testament, God and Christ, the incarnate Word of God, spoke by the Holy Spirit through men. They affirmed the writing of Paul to Timothy, "All Scripture is God-breathed and is useful for teaching, rebuking, correcting and training in righteousness" (2 Timothy 3:16). Unlike other doctrines, the authority of the Scripture was undebatable.

Belief in the absolute authority of the Scripture is foundational to your faith. I encourage you to study this lesson carefully and prayerfully so you will be able to assure others of the divine authorship and sureness of God's holy Word.

Bible Study

Testimony of Its Writers

The phrase, "thus saith the Lord," or its equivalent, occurs more than 2,000 times in the Old Testament.

1. Write out the statements concerning inspiration made by the following writers:

   David (2 Samuel 23:2)

   Isaiah (Isaiah 8:1,5,11)

   Jeremiah (Jeremiah 1:9)

Ezekiel (Ezekiel 3:4)

What is different about each? What is the same?

2. What two statements of Moses in Exodus 31:18 and 32:16 show that God actually wrote the Ten Commandments?

3. What statement made by David shows that the pattern for the temple was dictated by God (1 Chronicles 28:19)?

Testimony of Christ

The New Testament had not been written during Christ's earthly ministry, and His references to the Scriptures refer to the Old Testament writings. He never once denied or made light of Old Testament Scriptures; He related Himself to them as their fulfillment. He said:

> These are the Scriptures that testify about me (John 5:39).

1. How did Christ describe those who did not believe the Old Testament prophecies (Luke 24:25)?

2. What is the result of not believing in the Old Testament (John 5:46,47)?

3. What did Christ think of His responsibility concerning Old Testament prophecy (Matthew 5:17,18)?

4. What was Christ's view of the story of man's creation as recorded in Genesis (Matthew 19:4–6)?

5. What authority did Christ use to answer:
Satan (Matthew 4:4,7,10)?

Men (Matthew 22:29–32,43–46)?

6. Summarize Christ's attitude and view of the Old Testament.

Testimony of the Apostles

It is evident from their inspired writing that the apostles of Christ considered the Old Testament Scriptures prophetic and inseparable from the authority, power, and ministry of Christ.

1. *Peter.* From whom did the apostle Peter say the writings of the Old Testament came (2 Peter 1:21; Acts 1:16)?

How did Peter feel about the Old Testament historical account he recorded in 1 Peter 3:20?

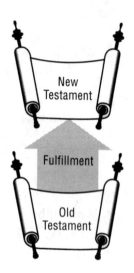

Who did Peter say were inspired by God (Acts 3:20,21)?

2. *Paul.* How much of the Old Testament is inspired by God, according to Paul in 2 Timothy 3:16?

What did Paul believe the Old Testament to be (Romans 3:2)?

3. *James.* Acceptance of the Old Testament writing is evidenced in the Book of James by references to whom?
2:21

2:25

5:11

5:17

4. *John.* One of the many evidences that John believed the Old Testament is his acceptance of which story (1 John 3:12)?

LIFE APPLICATION

1 The writers of the Old Testament, Jesus Christ the Son of God, the apostles of Christ, and the early church fathers all say of the Old Testament, "This is the inspired Word of God." What do you say? (See John 8:47 and 1 John 4:6.)

2 Describe how the information in this lesson gives you confidence in the authority of the Old Testament.

3 Write down several proofs of the authority of the Old Testament that you could use to explain to someone who doubts it.

4 Repeat the names of the five books of poetry until you have committed them to memory. Then write them here:

5 Review all the names of the books you learned earlier.

Authority of the New Testament

As you prepare to start this lesson, pick up your Bible and thumb through the pages of the New Testament. Have you ever thought about its origin and how its twenty-seven books were collected together into one volume?

Since the first of the books was probably not written until about A.D. 50, the church did not have a "New Testament" for the first twenty years following our Lord's ascension. Instead, the early Christians relied on the Old Testament and the eye-witness accounts of His disciples.

Christianity began with the preaching of Jesus but was spread word-of-mouth by the faithful witness of His followers. Eventually the oral gospel and the writings of the apostles to the churches were preserved for us in the books of the New Testament.

The New Testament grew book by book, beginning with the writings of Paul. As Paul established churches in new communities, he kept in touch with them by letter. Beginning with the letters to the Thessalonians, Paul corresponded with his churches until his death. His letters were copied, compiled,

Objective: To gain confidence in the Bible's authority by looking at the reliability of the New Testament

Read: Acts 21 and 22

Memorize: Matthew 24:35

and circulated among the churches until they became known throughout the Christian communities.

As the years passed and the number of living eye-witnesses became fewer, the Gospels were written to preserve their accounts. Mark wrote his Gospel first, followed by Matthew, Luke, and John.

In addition to Paul's letters and the Gospels, other epistles, the Book of Acts, and the Book of Revelation soon appeared until the church had in its possession all the books of our New Testament by the close of the first century.

These twenty-seven books, however, represent only a few of the numerous writings produced by the early Christians, many of which attempted to reinterpret the sayings and teachings of Christ. For more than two hundred years, the church fathers could not decide which of those works should be considered written under the guidance and inspiration of the Holy Spirit and thus be approved for reading in the public services of the church. The need for unity in belief and practice among Christians eventually led the fathers to separate the writings that were in harmony with the teachings of Jesus from those that were not.

The authoritative list of books developed slowly and gradually under the influence of the Holy Spirit until by the year 400 most Christians had accepted the twenty-seven books that now compose our New Testament. Today almost all of Christianity— Catholics and Protestant groups of many kinds—have placed their approval upon them.

"Heaven and Earth shall pass away ...not my Word."

Holy Bible

In 1874 the Scriptures were under severe attack by critics, and John W. Haley published a defense entitled *Alleged Discrepancies of the Bible*. In the preface he wrote:

>   Finally, let it be remembered that the Bible is neither dependent upon nor affected by the success or failure of

any book. Whatever may become of the latter, whatever may be the verdict passed upon it by an intelligent public, the Bible will stand. In the ages yet to be, when its present assailants and defenders are moldering in the dust, and when our very names are forgotten, (God's Word) will be, as it has been during the centuries past, the guide and solace of millions.

Bible Study

Authority Given the Apostles by Christ

1. What four things did Christ say the Holy Spirit would do for the apostles (John 16:12–15)?

1)

2)

3)

4)

Why do you think the apostles could not know all the truth at that time?

How would they in the future?

2. What authority did Christ give the apostles (John 17:18; 20:21)?

3. On what basis did Christ select the apostles to bear witness of Him (John 15:26,27; Luke 24:46–48)?

How did Paul fit in according to Acts 9:3–6; Acts 26:13–15, and 1 Corinthians 15:7–9?

4. What authority did Christ give Paul (Acts 26:15–18)?

How do we fit into this as witnesses?

The Apostles Wrote Under Christ's Authority

1. *Paul.* What does he call himself at the beginning of the book of Romans?

From whom did Paul receive what he preached (1 Corinthians 11:23; Galatians 1:11,12)?

What was Paul's authority and purpose (2 Corinthians 5:20)?

Read 2 Peter 3:15,16. What did Peter think about Paul's writings?

What did he think about those who misuse the New Testament?

2. *Writer of Hebrews.* Where did the writer of Hebrews get his authority (Hebrews 1:1,2)?

3. *James.* What did this half-brother of Jesus (Jesus's Father is God) call himself (James 1:1)?

4. *John.* What does John claim as the authority for writing his epistles (1 John 1:1–3)?

How was Revelation written (Revelation 1:1)?

5. *Jude.* What does this other half-brother of Jesus call himself in Jude 1?

What do you think Paul, James, and Jude meant by saying they were bondservants of Christ?

6. *Peter.* What does he call himself (1 Peter 1:1)?

What does Peter make known (2 Peter 1:16)?

7. On whose writings is the foundation of the church of Jesus Christ established (Ephesians 2:20)?

8. What is the gospel of Christ, according to the apostles (Romans 1:16)?

9. Why were the apostles confident that they wrote correctly about Christ (2 Corinthians 4:5,6)?

▪ LIFE APPLICATION

1 God has miraculously preserved His Word for us. Although the above study should convince us that the New Testament is the Word of God, what is your greatest assurance that it is God's Word (John 16:13; 8:47; 18:37)?

2 How does the information in this lesson help you trust the Bible more than you may have in the past?

How will you use the deeper trust in:
Witnessing?

Praying?

Daily living?

3 Commit to memory the names of the five books of the Major Prophets. Then write them here:

4 Review the names of all the other books you have previously learned.

The Power of God's Word

> I believe a knowledge of the Bible without a college education is more valuable than a college education without the Bible.
>
> —William Lyon Phelps, former professor at Yale University

❖

Objective: To experience the power of God's Word in our daily lives

Read: Acts 21 and 24

Memorize: Hebrews 4:12

Lila and her husband were expecting their fourth child and were looking forward to the new baby's arrival with eager anticipation. Then, unexpectedly, their dreams were shattered by a miscarriage.

Not only was Lila grieved by the loss of the child, it soon became apparent that her life was in grave danger. Serious complications suddenly became evident, and she was rushed by ambulance to the hospital.

Lila was vaguely aware of her surroundings as she slipped in and out of consciousness. Her family was at her side encouraging her, and many friends and loved ones were praying fervently.

During the crisis, she found it nearly impossible to focus her mind on anything except for one clear impression that persisted in her mind. "I can endure…I can survive…I can withstand…all things through Christ who strengthens me."

53

Somehow, in spite of the loss of blood and the close proximity of death, she was aware that she was not remembering the words just right. Yet intuitively she understood that God was promising to see her through.

Two weeks later, she returned home weakened but alive. While reading her Bible, she suddenly remembered the exact Scripture.

> I can do all things through Christ who strengthens me (Philippians 4:13, NKJ).

How she praised God for His Word, which had penetrated the fog of unconsciousness with a powerful promise of strength and provision!

In the Epistle to the Hebrews, Paul records:

> The word of God is living and active. Sharper than any double-edged sword, it penetrates even to dividing soul and spirit, joints and marrow; it judges the thoughts and attitudes of the heart (Hebrews 4:12).

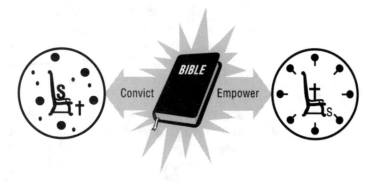

God's holy, inspired Word has several characteristics that guarantee powerful results.

First, *it is infused with the power of the Holy Spirit.* It has been said that a Bible that is falling apart usually belongs to a person who isn't. That is because God's Word is energetic and active, speaking to today's world and our own personal needs and circumstances.

Second, *God's Word is truth.* It awakens our conscience. With the power to reach into the private corners of our hearts, the Word bares our motives and secret feelings and reveals our hidden longings.

Third, *God's Word discerns our true character.* It exposes the weaknesses in our attitudes and conduct, enabling us to correct ourselves by the power of His Holy Spirit.

As you study this lesson, I urge you to begin hiding the Word of God in your heart, drawing upon its wisdom for your life. Remember that God's Word will never return to Him void, but will most certainly accomplish what it was sent to do. Share the Word with a friend, bearing witness to the faithfulness of our wonderful Lord and the power and authority of His Holy Spirit.

Bible Study

The Word of God

Tell what God's Word is or what it does, or both, according to the following Scripture references (use dictionary for definition of key words if needed).

1. What it is:

Hebrews 5:12–14

Philippians 2:16

Ephesians 6:17

2. What it does:

1 John 2:5

John 12:48

Romans 10:17

John 15:3

3. Both:
   1 Peter 1:23

   John 8:31,32

   John 17:17

   1 Peter 2:2

   Hebrews 4:12 (5 things)

How to Understand the Word of God

1. Read 1 Corinthians 2:14.

No one can understand the Word of God by his own ability. Why?

2. Describe in your own words a natural man's reaction to spiritual things.

3. Explain in your own words how one must come to understand the Word of God. See 1 Corinthians 2:7–12 and Romans 8:5–9.

Why do some individuals deny the authority of Scripture, the deity of Christ, the inspiration of the Bible, and other basic teachings in the Word of God?

What should be our response to them?

LIFE APPLICATION

1 When we approach the Word of God, what is the first thing we should understand (2 Peter 1:20,21)?

2 What is one way the power of the Bible manifests itself, according to 2 Timothy 3:15?

3 How have you experienced that power in your life recently?

4 The twelve books of the Minor Prophets are probably the most difficult of all to learn and remember. Give extra diligence to memorizing this division, then write the names here:

The Need for God's Word

Before I became a believer in Jesus Christ, God's Word didn't make any sense to me. I tried to read it occasionally during my high school and college days, but found it boring. Finally, I concluded that no really intelligent person could believe the Bible.

But when I became a Christian, my life was transformed, and my attitudes concerning the Scriptures changed. I realized that the Bible was truly the holy, inspired Word of God. For almost fifty years it has been more important to me than the thousands of books in my library combined.

Why is the Bible so important to the Christian? Let me share five basic reasons.

First, *the Word of God is divinely inspired.* The apostle Paul wrote, "All Scripture is God-breathed and is useful for teaching, rebuking, correcting and training in righteousness, so that the man of God may be thoroughly equipped for every good work" (2 Timothy 3:16).

Second, *the Scripture is the basis of our belief.* As the divinely-inspired Word, the Bible gives us God's perspective on how we should live. It offers His pardon for our sins, reveals His purpose for our lives, shows us

❖

Objective: To gain spiritual dependence on God's Word for daily Christian living

Read: Acts 25 and 26

Memorize: Psalm 119:105

how to live peacefully in a world of turmoil, and commands us to appropriate His power so we can be fruitful witnesses for our Lord Jesus Christ.

Many years ago, while I was a student at Fuller Theological Seminary, two gifted young evangelists came to speak during our chapel program. Both believed and preached the Word of God without questioning its authority. Later, however, they began to doubt that the Bible was truly inspired in every word.

One of these men finally rejected the integrity of the Scripture altogether. As a result, he had no moorings on which to base his life and ministry. He is now a skeptic and an outspoken opponent of the Christian faith.

The other young evangelist chose to believe that the Bible is truly the authoritative, inspired Word of God, and what he could not understand he entrusted to God and believed by faith.

Few remember the name of the first man. But the second is Billy Graham, whom God has used to touch the lives of millions around the world.

Third, *the Bible is God's love letter to man.* From Genesis to Revelation, it tells of God's great compassion for us and of His desire to have fellowship with us. John 3:16, perhaps the most beloved passage in the Bible, summarizes the depth of His love for us:

> God so loved the world that he gave his one and only Son, that whoever believes in him shall not perish but have eternal life.

Fourth, *the Bible reveals God's attributes.* It tells us that He is holy, sovereign, righteous, and just; that He is loving, merciful, and kind; that He is gracious, patient, and faithful. We have no trouble trusting Him if we really understand who He is and how holy, loving, and wonderful His purposes are for us.

Fifth, *God's Word teaches us how to live holy lives and to be fruitful witnesses for our Lord.* The more we read and meditate on His precious Word—and let His Holy Spirit control our lives—the more fruitful we become.

Are you spending time meditating on God's Word daily? If not, let me encourage you to begin today. As you study this lesson, ask God to reveal Himself to you in a fresh, new way and let Him speak to your heart of His will for you. I encourage you to depend on God's Word for your daily Christian living.

Bible Study

What We Should Know About the Bible
Read Psalm 119.

1. What does the psalmist call God's Word in the following verses of Psalm 119?

    Verse 1

    Verse 2

    Verse 4

    Verse 5

    Verse 6

    Verse 7

    Verse 43

Verse 72

Verse 105

Verse 123

2. What does this tell you of the importance of knowing God's Word?

3. When does God discipline His children (Psalm 119:126)?

4. What value does the Word have for us (Psalm 119:72)?

5. What is necessary in order to learn the Word (Psalm 119:73)?

How God's Word Affects Our Feelings

1. According to these verses in Psalm 119, what does the psalmist recognize is accomplished by respecting and learning God's Word?

Verse 7

Verse 8

Verse 9

2. From Psalm 119:10–16, list at least three attitudes of the psalmist that show his love for the Word of God.

1)

2)

3)

3. Why is adversity sometimes good for us (Psalm 119:67 and 71)?

4. From these verses in Psalm 119, what is the reaction of those who love Christ when His Word is not kept?

Verse 136

Verse 158

5. How can we have great peace (Psalm 119:165)?

Results of Appropriating God's Word

1. Read these verses in Psalm 119, and write what affect the Word has on us when we do the following:

Know and memorize the Word (verse 98)

Meditate on it (verse 99)

Obey it (verse 100)

Follow it (verse 105)

What does the Word give us (verse 130)?

2. According to Psalm 119, what should we do as a result of appropriating the Word?
Verse 11

Verse 32

Verse 63

Verse 74

Verse 157

Verse 176

LIFE APPLICATION

1 What impresses you most about Psalm 119?

2 List three ways in which you recognize your personal need for God's Word today.

3 Many people can recite the four books of the Gospels. Can you? Add the one book of New Testament history, and write all five books here:

Since this division is quite easy, go ahead to the next division, the Pauline epistles and Hebrews. That division is harder to learn so you should get started on it now.

Private Bible Study Methods

Martin Luther said he studied his Bible in the same way he gathered apples. He encourages us to:

Search the Bible as a whole, shaking the whole tree. Read it rapidly, as you would any other book. Then shake every limb—study book after book.

Then shake every branch, giving attention to the chapters when they do not break the sense. Then shake each twig by a careful study of the paragraphs and sentences. And you will be rewarded if you will look under each leaf by searching the meaning of the words.

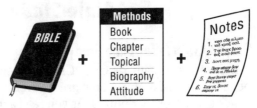

❖

Objective: To establish good habits of regular, systematic study of the Bible

Read: Acts 27 and 28

Memorize: Colossians 3:16,17

The *Thompson Chain Reference Bible* gives this suggestion:

Study the Bible as a traveler who seeks to obtain a thorough and experimental knowledge of a new country.

Go over its vast fields to truth; descend into its valleys; climb its mountains of vision; follow its streams of inspiration; enter its halls of instruction; visit its wondrous portrait galleries.

Remember that many doctrinal errors have grown out of a lack of spiritual perspective, or a narrow view of scriptural truth. The Savior says, "Ye do err, not knowing the Scriptures, nor the power of God."

Seek to understand the deep things of God. Study "The Word" as a miner digs for gold, or as a diver plunges into the depths of the sea for pearls.

Most great truths do not lie upon the surface. They must be brought up into the light by patient toil.

Every time you and I read and study God's Word carefully, we are building up our storehouse of faith. When we memorize the Word, our faith is being increased.

Reading the Bible is vital for every Christian. How can we learn about God or grow spiritually if we do not spend time studying the Book in which He has made Himself known to us?

Taking a few minutes each day to read a chapter is a good way to start. But we should also block out extended periods of time for exploring God's Word and reflecting on what He is saying to us.

Bible Study

Proper Attitude for Bible Study

When you personally received Christ as your Savior and Lord, you began a great adventure. That great adventure is mapped out in the pages of the Holy Scriptures. As you read and study the Bible in the power of the Holy Spirit, you will receive meaning, strength, direction, and power for your life. You will learn and claim the many great promises God has reserved for His own.

Approach the Bible in prayer; with reverence, awe, and expectancy; with a willing mind; and with a thirst for truth, righteousness, and fullness in the Lord Jesus Christ. When you come with a humble and contrite heart, you can trust God the Holy Spirit to reveal God's truth to you, and you will experience the cleansing power of His eternal Word.

Above all, as you study God's Word, be eager to obey all that He commands, and rejoice in the knowledge that you are an ambassador for Christ, seeking men in His name to be reconciled to God.

1. How do you feel about Bible study?

2. What do you see at this point as your main purpose in studying God's Word?

3. Have you established a definite goal regarding Bible study?

Tools Needed

First, obtain at least two translations of the Bible. Study the various translations. You would not expect to learn much about the physical laws of our universe without diligent and persistent study. Should you expect to acquire much knowledge of God and the unsearchable riches of His Word without studying with equal diligence and persistence?

As funds are available, you will want to secure a topical Bible, a concordance, and a Bible dictionary. Additional Bible study books are helpful and can be added as convenient. However, always remember, Bible study involves just that—studying the Bible. The other items are merely tools to assist you in getting the rich truths God has for you in His Word.

As you consider each study of the Scriptures, may I suggest you record God's Word to you in a journal. This will not only result in a deeper, more serious study, it will also give you a written record of how God speaks to you and of your response to Him.

1. List the tools you now have.

2. List the additional tools you desire in the order in which you plan to obtain them.

Suggested Methods

1. *Book study.* The Bible contains many books. Yet the divine plan of God to redeem men in Christ Jesus runs through the whole of it. Be careful to consider each book as a part of the whole. Read it through. Following these suggestions will help make your study more meaningful:

   ◆ *Mark and underline* as God speaks to you through His Word.

   ◆ *Outline* it.

   ◆ *List* the names of the principal characters; tell who they are and their significance.

   ◆ *Select* from each chapter key verses to memorize and copy them on a card to carry with you.

   ◆ *List* teachings to obey and promises to claim.

   ◆ *Consider* the characteristics revealed of God the Father, God the Son, and God the Holy Spirit.

   Which book would you particularly like to study using this method? (It is best to start with one of the shorter ones.)

2. *Chapter study.* To get a grasp of the chapter, answer the following questions:

- ◆ What is the principal subject of the chapter?
- ◆ What is the leading lesson?
- ◆ What is the key verse? (Memorize it.)
- ◆ Who are the principal characters?
- ◆ What does it teach about God the Father?
- ◆ What does it teach about Jesus Christ?
- ◆ What does it teach about the Holy Spirit?
- ◆ Is there any example for me to follow?
- ◆ Is there any error for me to avoid?
- ◆ Is there any duty for me to perform?
- ◆ Is there any promise for me to claim?
- ◆ Is there any prayer for me to echo?

Chose a chapter from the book, and apply these questions.

3. *Topical study.* Take an important subject—such as grace, truth, prayer, faith, assurance, justification, regeneration, or peace—and, using a topical Bible and a concordance, study the scope of the topic throughout the Bible.

You will find it necessary to divide each topic into subtopics as you accumulate material; for example, forms of prayer, prayer promises, examples of prayer in Scripture, Christ's teaching on prayer, Christ's ministry as we pray, the ministry of the Holy Spirit in prayer.

What topic do you plan to study first?

How much time have you scheduled for it?

4. *Biographical study.* There are 2,930 people mentioned in the Bible. The lives of many of these make extremely interesting biographical studies. Why is it important to study the characters of the Bible (1 Corinthians 10:11; Romans 15:4)?

Using a concordance, topical Bible, or the proper name index in your Bible, look up every reference in the Bible of someone you would like to study.

Name the person you would like to study.

State your reason for choosing that particular person.

Answer the following questions:

◆ What was the social and political atmosphere in which he (or she) lived?

◆ How did that affect his life?

◆ What do we know of his family?

◆ What kind of training did he have in his youth?

◆ What was accomplished by him during his life?

◆ Was there a great crisis in his life? If so, how did he face it?

◆ What were his outstanding character traits?

◆ Who were his friends? What kind of people were they?

◆ What influence did they have on him?

◆ What influence did he have on them?

◆ Does his life show any development of character?

◆ What was his experience with God? Notice his prayer life, faith, service to God, knowledge of God's Word, courage in witnessing, and attitude toward the worship of God.

- ◆ Were any particular faults evident in his life?
- ◆ Was there any outstanding sin in his life?
- ◆ Under what circumstances did he commit this sin?
- ◆ What was its nature and its effect on his future life?
- ◆ What were his children like?
- ◆ Was there some lesson in this person's life that will help to enrich your life?

By the time you complete the studies outlined in this series of booklets, you will have been introduced to each of these four methods. You already have taken the first step in the book study method by reading the Book of Acts. Lessons 2 and 4 of *Step 2: The Christian and the Abundant Life* were chapter studies. You will soon be ready to apply these as well as the other two methods to more advanced work in your own individual Bible study.

LIFE APPLICATION

1 Which method interests you most now?

2 How do you expect to benefit from serious study of the Bible?

3 Select one method and use it over the next week. Use the other methods in the following weeks.

4 Complete your memorization of the Pauline epistles and the last book of prophecy. Write them all here:

Pauline epistles and Hebrews

General epistles and prophecy

Remember, always study the Bible with the following:
◆ A pencil
◆ A notebook
◆ A prayer
◆ A purpose

Recap

The following questions will help you review this Step. If necessary, reread the appropriate lesson(s).

1. On a piece of paper, write the divisions of the books of the Bible and the names of each book in each division. Review any division you do not know well.

2. How would you explain the statement, "Christ is the central person of the Bible?"

3. Who do you think is the real source of the authority of the Scripture?

Describe how this is evident in biblical history.

Reread: Acts 15–28

Review: Verses memorized

4. Name at least three things the Word of God accomplishes that indicate its supernatural power.

1)

2)

3)

Write down several changes that the Bible has made in your life. Be specific.

5. Why do you need the Word of God?

6. What steps do you still need to take to be fully prepared for serious study of the Bible?

7. Review the names of the books of the Bible and write them one final time. Be sure the spelling is correct.

LIFE APPLICATION

❶ Begin a journal of what you are learning through your Bible study. Buy a small notebook and record:

- ◆ The portion of Scripture you are studying
- ◆ The method you are using

For each day of study, record the following:

- ◆ Date
- ◆ Lesson that is important to you
- ◆ How you can apply it to your life
- ◆ Results of previous lessons you have applied to your daily situations

Also, write down prayer requests and answers as well as verses you have memorized.

When you finish the study, begin again with another portion of Scripture.

❷ Periodically review your journal to see how you are growing spiritually and to remind yourself of important lessons you have learned.

Resources to Help You Study the Bible

Holman Bible Dictionary, Trent C. Butler, editor. Published by Holman Bible Publishers, Nashville, TN.

The Illustrated Bible Handbook by Edward P. Blair. Published by Abingdon Press, Nashville, TN.

Life Application Bible (Living Bible Version). Published by Tyndale House Publishers, Wheaton, IL.

Halley's Bible Handbook, Revised Edition by Henry H. Halley. Published by Zondervan Publishing House, Grand Rapids, MI.

What the Bible Is All About by Henrietta Mears. Published by Regal Books, Ventura, CA.

Step 9: Exploring the Old Testament, Ten Basic Steps Toward Christian Maturity by Bill Bright. Published by NewLife Publications, Orlando, FL.

Step 10: Exploring the New Testament, Ten Basic Steps Toward Christian Maturity by Bill Bright. Published by NewLife Publications, Orlando, FL.

Available through your local Christian bookstore, mail-order catalog distributor, or NewLife Publications.

Ten Basic Steps Toward Christian Maturity

*Eleven easy-to-use individual guides to help you understand
the basics of the Christian faith*

INTRODUCTION:
The Uniqueness of Jesus

Explains who Jesus Christ is. Reveals the secret of His power to turn you into a victorious, fruitful Christian.

STEP 1: The Christian Adventure

Shows you how to enjoy a full, abundant, purposeful, and fruitful life in Christ.

STEP 2: The Christian and the Abundant Life

Explores the Christian way of life—what it is and how it works practically.

STEP 3: The Christian and the Holy Spirit

Teaches who the Holy Spirit is, how to be filled with the Spirit, and how to make the Spirit-filled life a moment-by-moment reality in your life.

STEP 4: The Christian and Prayer

Reveals the true purpose of prayer and shows how the Father, Son, and Holy Spirit work together to answer your prayers.

STEP 5: The Christian and the Bible

Talks about the Bible—how we got it, its authority, and its power to help the believer. Offers methods for studying the Bible more effectively.

STEP 6: The Christian and Obedience

Learn why it is so important to obey God and how to live daily in His grace. Discover the secret to personal purity and power as a Chris-

tian and why you need not fear what others think of you.

STEP 7: The Christian and Witnessing

Shows you how to witness effectively. Includes a reproduction of the *Four Spiritual Laws* and explains how to share them.

STEP 8: The Christian and Giving

Discover God's plan for your financial life, how to stop worrying about money, and how to trust God for your finances.

STEP 9: Exploring the Old Testament

Features a brief survey of the Old Testament. Shows what God did to prepare the way for Jesus Christ and the redemption of all who receive Him as Savior and Lord.

STEP 10: Exploring the New Testament

Surveys each of the New Testament books. Shows the essence of the gospel and highlights the exciting beginning of the Christian church.

Leader's Guide

The ultimate resource for even the most inexperienced, timid, and fearful person asked to lead a group study in the basics of the Christian life. Contains questions and answers from the *Ten Basic Steps* Study Guides.

A Handbook for Christian Maturity

Combines the eleven-booklet series into one practical, easy-to-follow volume. Excellent for personal or group study.

*Available through your local Christian bookstore,
mail-order catalog distributor, or NewLife Publications.*

About the Author

BILL BRIGHT is founder and president of Campus Crusade for Christ International. Serving in 152 major countries representing 98 percent of the world's population, he and his dedicated associates of nearly 50,000 full-time staff, associate staff, and trained volunteers have introduced tens of millions of people to Jesus Christ, discipling millions to live Spirit-filled, fruitful lives of purpose and power for the glory of God.

Dr. Bright did graduate study at Princeton and Fuller Theological seminaries from 1946 to 1951. The recipient of many national and international awards, including five honorary doctorates, he is the author of numerous books and publications committed to helping fulfill the Great Commission. His special focus is New Life 2000, an international effort to help reach more than six billion people with the gospel of our Lord Jesus Christ and help fulfill the Great Commission by the year 2000.